America's
NATIONAL PARKS
2022

America's National Parks 2022 Weekly Engagement
© 2021 Ziga Media, LLC

Design © Ziga Media, LLC
Print production by Laura Livingston

Ziga Media, LLC
5 Overbrook Lane, Darien, CT 06820
203.656.0076
zigamedia.com

ISBN 978-1-63771-050-0

Printed in South Korea

Lunar phases and seasons are given in Universal Time.

● New Moon   ◗ First Quarter Moon   ○ Full Moon   ◖ Last Quarter Moon

(ACT AUS) Australian Capital Territory   (AUS) Australia   (CAN) Canada
(FRA) France   (IRL) Ireland   (NSW) New South Wales, Australia
(NT AUS) Northern Territory, Australia   (NZL) New Zealand   (Qland) Queensland, Australia
(S AUS) South Australia   (SCT) Scotland   (TAS AUS) Tasmania, Australia
(UK) United Kingdom: England, Northern Ireland, Scotland, Wales
(USA) United States   (Victoria AUS) Victoria, Australia   (W AUS) Western Australia

Please note that while we have made every effort to ensure the accuracy
of the information presented in this calendar, we cannot be held liable
for any errors, omissions, or inconsistencies.

For calendars, journals, and puzzles go to
zigamedia.com • 203.656.0076

PERSONAL DATA

Name

_____

Address

_____

_____

Tel
_____
Cell
_____
Fax
_____
Email
_____
Social Media
_____

Company

_____

Address

_____

_____

Tel
_____
Fax
_____
Email
_____
Social Media
_____

Notes

_____

_____

_____

_____

_____

_____

INTERNATIONAL DIALING CODES

Country/City	Code	Country/City	Code	Country/City	Code	Country/City	Code
Afghanistan*	93	British West Indies		Cyprus	357	Guyana	592
Kabul	20	Anguilla*	1+264	Nicosia	22	Georgetown	2
Albania	355	British Virgin Islands*		Czech Republic	420	Haiti*	509
Tiranë	4		1+284	Prague	2	Honduras*	504
Algeria	213	Cayman Islands*		Denmark*	45	Hong Kong	852
Algiers	21		1+345	Dominican Republic*		Hungary	36
American Samoa*	684	Montserrat*	1+664		1+809	Budapest	1
Andorra*	376	Turks & Caicos*			1+829	Iceland	354
Argentina	54		1+649		1+849	India	91
Buenos Aires	11	Brunei	673	Ecuador	593	Kolkata	33
Aruba	297	Bandar Seri		Quito	2	Mumbai	22
Australia	61	Begawan	2	Egypt	20	New Delhi	11
Melbourne	3	Bulgaria	359	Cairo	2	Indonesia	62
Sydney	2	Plovdiv	32	El Salvador*	503	Jakarta	21
Austria	43	Sofia	2	Estonia	372	Iran	98
Salzburg	662	Varna	52	Ethiopia	251	Tehran	21
Vienna	1	Cambodia	855	Addis Ababa	11	Iraq	964
Azerbaijan	994	Phnom Penh	23	Fiji*	679	Baghdad	1
Baku	12	Siem Reap	63	Finland	358	Ireland	353
Bahamas*	242	Cameroon*	237	Helsinki	9	Dublin	1
Bahrain*	973	Canada**		France	33	Killarney	64
Bangladesh	880	Montreal	514, 438	Paris	1	Tipperary	62
Dhaka	2	Ottawa	613, 343	Northeast France	3	Israel	972
Barbados*	246	Quebec	418, 581	Northwest France	2	Haifa	4
Belarus	375	Toronto	416, 437,	Southeast France	4	Jerusalem	2
Brest	162		647	Southwest France	5	Tel Aviv	3
Minsk	17	Vancouver	236, 778,	French Antilles*	596	Italy	39
Belgium	32		604	French Polynesia*	689	Florence	55
Antwerp	3	Chile	56	Gabon*	241	Milan	2
Bruges	50	Santiago	2	Germany	49	Rome	6
Brussels	2	China	86	Berlin	30	Venice	41
Liège	4	Beijing	10	Bonn	228	Jamaica*	1+876
Belize	501	Guangzhou	20	Cologne	221	Japan	81
Belmopan	8	Shanghai	21	Dresden	351	Hiroshima	82
Bermuda*	441	Colombia	57	Frankfurt	69, 335	Kawasaki	44
Bolivia	591	Bogotá	1	Hanover	511	Nagoya	52
Santa Cruz	3	Costa Rica*	506	Munich	89	Tokyo	3
Bosnia &		Côte d'Ivoire*	225	Nuremberg	911	Yokohama	45
Herzogovina	387	Croatia	385	Gibraltar*	350	Jordan	962
Sarajevo	33	Zagreb	1	Greece	30	Amman	6
Brazil	55	Cuba	53	Athens	21	Kenya	254
Brasilia	61	Guantánamo	21	Greenland	299	Nairobi	20
Rio de Janeiro	21	Havana	7	Guam*	1+671	Korea, South	82
São Paulo	11	Curaçao	599	Guatemala*	502	Seoul	2

To place an international telephone call, dial the international access code (011 in the U.S.), the country code number, and then the local number.
*City routing code not required.
**International access code not required when dialing from the United States.

INTERNATIONAL DIALING CODES

Kosovo	383	Rotterdam	10	Mecca	2	Istanbul	212, 216
Pristina	38	The Hague	70	Riyadh	1	Uganda	256
Kuwait*	965	Utrecht	30	Senegal	221	Kampala	41
Latvia	371	New Caledonia	687	Serbia	381	Ukraine	380
Riga	7	New Zealand	64	Belgrade	11	Kiev	44
Lebanon	961	Auckland	9	Sierra Leone	232	Odessa	48
Beirut	1	Christchurch	3	Freetown	22	United Arab	
Tripoli	6	Wellington	4	Singapore	65	Emirates	971
Lesotho*	266	Nicaragua	505	Slovenia	386	Abu Dhabi	2
Liberia*	231	Managua	2	Ljubljana	1	Dubai	4
Libya	218	Nigeria	234	South Africa	27	United Kingdom	44
Tripoli	21	Abuja	9	Cape Town	21	Belfast	28
Liechtenstein*	423	Lagos	1	Johannesburg	11	Birmingham	121
Lithuania	370	Norway	47	Spain	34	Cardiff	29
Kuanas	37	Oman	968	Barcelona	93	Edinburgh	131
Vilnius	5, 521	Pakistan	92	Madrid	91	Glasgow	141
Luxembourg*	352	Islamabad	51	Seville	95	Liverpool	151
Macedonia	389	Palestine	970	Sri Lanka	94	London	20
Skopje	2	Gaza	8	Kandy	8	Manchester	161
Madagascar	261	Hebron	2	St. Maarten	1+721	United States	
Antananarivo	22	Panama	507	Suriname	597	of America	1
Malawi*	265	Papua New Guinea		Swaziland	268	Uruguay	598
Malaysia	60		675	Lobamba	416	Montevideo	2
Kuala Lumpur	3	Paraguay	595	Sweden	46	U.S. Virgin Islands*	
Maldives*	960	Asunción	21	Gothenburg	31		1+340
Mexico	52	Peru	51	Stockholm	8	Vatican City	39
Acapulco	744	Lima	1	Switzerland	41	Venezuela	58
Cancún	998	Philippines	63	Basel	61	Caracas	212
Mexico City	55	Manila	2	Geneva	22	San Cristóbal	276
Moldova	373	Poland	48	Lausanne	21	Valencia	241
Monaco*	377	Warsaw	22	Zurich	43, 44	Vietnam	84
Morocco	212	Portugal	351	Syria	963	Da Nang	51, 511
Casablanca	22	Lisbon	21	Damascus	11	Hanoi	4
Marrakech	44	Porto	22	Taiwan	886	Ho Chi Minh City	8
Rabat	37	Puerto Rico*	1+787	Taipei	2	Yemen	967
Mozambique	258		1+939	Tanzania	255	Sana'a	1
Maputo	21	Qatar*	974	Dar es Salaam	22	Zambia	260
Namibia	264	Romania	40	Zanzibar	24	Lusaka	1
Windhoek	61	Bucharest	21	Thailand	66	Zimbabwe	263
Nepal	977	Russia	7	Bangkok	2	Harare	4
Janakpur	41, 46	Moscow	495, 499	Tunisia	216		
Kathmandu	1	St. Petersburg	812	Tunis	1, 71		
Netherlands, The	31	Samoa*	685	Turkey	90		
Amsterdam	20	Saudi Arabia	966	Ankara	312		

WORLD TIME DIFFERENCES

Abu Dhabi	+4	Frankfurt	+1	Nairobi	+3
Accra	0	Freetown	0	New Delhi	+5½
Addis Ababa	+3	Geneva	+1	New York	−5
Alexandria	+2	Glasgow	0	Oslo	+1
Algiers	+1	Halifax	−4	Ottawa	−5
Amman	+2	Harare	+2	Paris	+1
Amsterdam	+1	Havana	−5	Port-au-Prince	−5
Anchorage	−9	Helsinki	+2	Prague	+1
Antigua and Barbuda	−4	Ho Chi Minh City	+7	Pyongyang	+9
Athens	+2	Hong Kong	+8	Reykjavik	0
Atlanta	−5	Honolulu	−10	Rio de Janeiro	−3
Auckland	+12	Houston	−6	Riyadh	+3
Azores	−1	Islamabad	+5	Rome	+1
Baghdad	+3	Istanbul	+3	San Juan	−4
Baku	+4	Jakarta	+7	Santiago	−4
Bangkok	+7	Jerusalem	+2	São Paulo	−3
Barcelona	+1	Johannesburg	+2	Sarajevo	+1
Basra	+3	Kabul	+4½	Saskatoon	-6
Beijing	+8	Karachi	+5	Seoul	+9
Beirut	+2	Kathmandu	+5¾	Shanghai	+8
Belfast	0	Khartoum	+2	Singapore	+8
Belize City	−6	Kolkata	+5½	Sofia	+2
Berlin	+1	Kuala Lumpur	+8	Stockholm	+1
Bern	+1	Kuwait City	+3	St. Louis	−6
Bogotá	−5	Lagos	+1	St. Petersburg	+3
Brussels	+1	La Paz	−7	Sydney	+10
Budapest	+1	Lima	−5	Taipei	+8
Buenos Aires	−3	Lisbon	0	Tehran	+3½
Cairo	+2	Ljubljana	+1	Timbuktu	0
Calgary	−7	London	0	Tokyo	+9
Caracas	−4	Los Angeles	−8	Toronto	−5
Casablanca	+1	Madrid	+1	Tunis	+1
Chicago	−6	Managua	−6	Ulaanbaatar	+8
Copenhagen	+1	Manila	+8	Vancouver	−8
Curaçao	−4	Martinique	−4	Vienna	+1
Dakar	0	Melbourne	+10	Vladivostok	+10
Damascus	+2	Mexico City	−6	Volgograd	+4
Dar es Salaam	+3	Mogadishu	+3	Warsaw	+1
Denver	−7	Montevideo	−3	Winnipeg	−6
Dublin	0	Montreal	−5	Yangon	+6½
Edinburgh	0	Moscow	+3	Yokohama	+9
Edmonton	−7	Mumbai	+5½	Zurich	+1

Time differences indicate Standard Time offset from Universal Time (UT, formerly Greenwich Mean Time). For example, New York (Eastern Standard Time) subtracts 5 hours from UT.

WEIGHTS & MEASURES

LENGTH

1 inch (in)		= 2.54 cm
1 foot (ft)	= 12 in	= 0.3048 m
1 yard (yd)	= 3 ft	= 0.9144 m
1 mile (mi)	= 1760 yd	= 1.6093 km
1 nautical mile	= 6,076.115 ft	= 1.852 km
1 millimeter (mm)		= 0.0394 in
1 centimeter (cm)	= 10 mm	= 0.3937 in
1 decimeter (dm)	= 10 cm	= 3.937 in
1 meter (m)	= 100 cm	= 1.0936 yd
1 kilometer (km)	= 1,000 m	= 0.6214 mi

MASS

1 ounce (oz)	= 437.5 grains	= 28.349 g
1 pound (lb)	= 16 oz	= 0.4536 kg
1 short ton	= 2,000 lbs	= 0.9072 t
1 long ton	= 2,240 lbs	= 1.0160 t
1 gram (g)	= 1,000 mg	= 0.0352 oz
1 kilogram (kg)	= 1,000 g	= 2.2046 lb
1 metric ton (t)	= 1,000 kg	= 1.1023 short tons

AREA

1 square inch (in²)		= 6.4516 cm²
1 square foot (ft²)	= 144 in²	= 0.0929 m²
1 square yard (yd²)	= 9 ft²	= 0.8361 m²
1 acre	= 4840 yd²	= 4046.87 m²
1 square mile (mi²)	= 640 acres	= 2.59 km²
1 square centimeter (cm²)	= 100 mm²	= 0.1550 in²
1 square meter (m²)	= 10,000 cm²	= 1.1959 yd²
1 hectare (ha)	= 10,000 m²	= 2.471 acres
1 square kilometer (km²)	= 100 ha	= 0.3861 mi²

CAPACITY

1 US dry pint (pt)	= 0.5 dry qt	= 0.5506 l
1 US dry quart (qt)	= 2 US dry pt	= 1.101 l
1 US bushel (bu)	= 64 US dry pt	= 35.239 l
1 US fluid ounce (fl oz)	= 0.031 liquid qt	= 29.573 ml
1 US liquid pint (pt)	= 0.5 liquid qt	= 0.4731 l
1 US liquid quart (qt)	= 2 US liquid pt	= 0.9463 l
1 US gallon	= 4 US liquid qt	= 3.7854 l
1 milliliter (ml)	= 0.001 l	= 0.0338 fl oz
1 centiliter (cl)	= 10 ml	= 0.338 fl oz
1 liter (l)	= 100 cl	= 0.2641 US gallon

VOLUME

1 cubic inch (in³)		= 16.387 cm³
1 cubic foot (ft³)	= 1728 in³	= 0.0283 m³
1 cubic yard (yd³)	= 27 ft³	= 0.7645 m³
1 cubic centimeter (cm³)	= 0.0610 in³	
1 cubic decimeter (dm³)	= 1,000 cm³	= 0.0353 ft³
1 cubic meter (m³)	= 1,000 dm³	= 1.3079 yd³

HOUSEHOLD CAPACITY

1 teaspoon	= ⅙ fluid oz	= 4.9 ml
1 tablespoon	= ½ fluid oz	= 14.8 ml
1 cup	= 8 fluid oz	= 236.6 ml
1 pint (2 cups)	= 16 fluid oz	= 473.2 ml
1 quart (2 pints)	= 32 fluid oz	= 946.4 ml
1 gallon (4 quarts)	= 128 fluid oz	= 3.785 l

2022

JANUARY

S	M	T	W	T	F	S
						1
2	3	4	5	6	7	8
9	10	11	12	13	14	15
16	17	18	19	20	21	22
23	24	25	26	27	28	29
30	31					

FEBRUARY

S	M	T	W	T	F	S
		1	2	3	4	5
6	7	8	9	10	11	12
13	14	15	16	17	18	19
20	21	22	23	24	25	26
27	28					

MARCH

S	M	T	W	T	F	S
		1	2	3	4	5
6	7	8	9	10	11	12
13	14	15	16	17	18	19
20	21	22	23	24	25	26
27	28	29	30	31		

APRIL

S	M	T	W	T	F	S
					1	2
3	4	5	6	7	8	9
10	11	12	13	14	15	16
17	18	19	20	21	22	23
24	25	26	27	28	29	30

MAY

S	M	T	W	T	F	S
1	2	3	4	5	6	7
8	9	10	11	12	13	14
15	16	17	18	19	20	21
22	23	24	25	26	27	28
29	30	31				

JUNE

S	M	T	W	T	F	S
			1	2	3	4
5	6	7	8	9	10	11
12	13	14	15	16	17	18
19	20	21	22	23	24	25
26	27	28	29	30		

JULY

S	M	T	W	T	F	S
					1	2
3	4	5	6	7	8	9
10	11	12	13	14	15	16
17	18	19	20	21	22	23
24	25	26	27	28	29	30
31						

AUGUST

S	M	T	W	T	F	S
	1	2	3	4	5	6
7	8	9	10	11	12	13
14	15	16	17	18	19	20
21	22	23	24	25	26	27
28	29	30	31			

SEPTEMBER

S	M	T	W	T	F	S
				1	2	3
4	5	6	7	8	9	10
11	12	13	14	15	16	17
18	19	20	21	22	23	24
25	26	27	28	29	30	

OCTOBER

S	M	T	W	T	F	S
						1
2	3	4	5	6	7	8
9	10	11	12	13	14	15
16	17	18	19	20	21	22
23	24	25	26	27	28	29
30	31					

NOVEMBER

S	M	T	W	T	F	S
		1	2	3	4	5
6	7	8	9	10	11	12
13	14	15	16	17	18	19
20	21	22	23	24	25	26
27	28	29	30			

DECEMBER

S	M	T	W	T	F	S
				1	2	3
4	5	6	7	8	9	10
11	12	13	14	15	16	17
18	19	20	21	22	23	24
25	26	27	28	29	30	31

2023

JANUARY

S	M	T	W	T	F	S
1	2	3	4	5	6	7
8	9	10	11	12	13	14
15	16	17	18	19	20	21
22	23	24	25	26	27	28
29	30	31				

FEBRUARY

S	M	T	W	T	F	S
			1	2	3	4
5	6	7	8	9	10	11
12	13	14	15	16	17	18
19	20	21	22	23	24	25
26	27	28				

MARCH

S	M	T	W	T	F	S
			1	2	3	4
5	6	7	8	9	10	11
12	13	14	15	16	17	18
19	20	21	22	23	24	25
26	27	28	29	30	31	

APRIL

S	M	T	W	T	F	S
						1
2	3	4	5	6	7	8
9	10	11	12	13	14	15
16	17	18	19	20	21	22
23	24	25	26	27	28	29
30						

MAY

S	M	T	W	T	F	S
	1	2	3	4	5	6
7	8	9	10	11	12	13
14	15	16	17	18	19	20
21	22	23	24	25	26	27
28	29	30	31			

JUNE

S	M	T	W	T	F	S
				1	2	3
4	5	6	7	8	9	10
11	12	13	14	15	16	17
18	19	20	21	22	23	24
25	26	27	28	29	30	

JULY

S	M	T	W	T	F	S
						1
2	3	4	5	6	7	8
9	10	11	12	13	14	15
16	17	18	19	20	21	22
23	24	25	26	27	28	29
30	31					

AUGUST

S	M	T	W	T	F	S
		1	2	3	4	5
6	7	8	9	10	11	12
13	14	15	16	17	18	19
20	21	22	23	24	25	26
27	28	29	30	31		

SEPTEMBER

S	M	T	W	T	F	S
					1	2
3	4	5	6	7	8	9
10	11	12	13	14	15	16
17	18	19	20	21	22	23
24	25	26	27	28	29	30

OCTOBER

S	M	T	W	T	F	S
1	2	3	4	5	6	7
8	9	10	11	12	13	14
15	16	17	18	19	20	21
22	23	24	25	26	27	28
29	30	31				

NOVEMBER

S	M	T	W	T	F	S
			1	2	3	4
5	6	7	8	9	10	11
12	13	14	15	16	17	18
19	20	21	22	23	24	25
26	27	28	29	30		

DECEMBER

S	M	T	W	T	F	S
					1	2
3	4	5	6	7	8	9
10	11	12	13	14	15	16
17	18	19	20	21	22	23
24	25	26	27	28	29	30
31						

DECEMBER 2021

20 Monday

---

21 Tuesday   *First Day of Winter*

---

22 Wednesday

---

23 Thursday

---

24 Friday

Christmas Eve
Christmas Day (Observed) (USA)

---

25 Saturday   *Christmas Day*

---

26 Sunday

First Day of Kwanzaa • Boxing Day
St. Stephen's Day • Proclamation Day (Observed) (S AUS)

DECEMBER 2021

S	M	T	W	T	F	S
			1	2	3	4
5	6	7	8	9	10	11
12	13	14	15	16	17	18
19	20	21	22	23	24	25
26	27	28	29	30	31	

DECEMBER 2021 / JANUARY 2022

Christmas Day (Observed) (AUS, CAN, IRL, NZL, UK)

Monday 27 ☾

Boxing Day (Observed)
Proclamation Day (S AUS)

Tuesday 28

Wednesday 29

Thursday 30

New Year's Eve
New Year's Day (Observed) (USA)

Friday 31

New Year's Day
Last Day of Kwanzaa

Saturday 1

Day after New Year's Day (NZL, SCT)

Sunday 2 ●

JANUARY 2022						
S	M	T	W	T	F	S
						1
2	3	4	5	6	7	8
9	10	11	12	13	14	15
16	17	18	19	20	21	22
23	24	25	26	27	28	29
30	31					

JANUARY

| 3 | Monday | *New Year's Day (Observed, except USA)* |

| 4 | Tuesday | *Day after New Year's Day (Observed) (NZL, SCT)* |

| 5 | Wednesday | |

| 6 | Thursday | *Epiphany* |

| 7 | Friday | |

| 8 | Saturday | |

| 9 | Sunday ☽ | |

A snowglobe perspective of Crater Lake, Crater Lake National Park, Oregon
© *Matthew Connolly/Shutterstock.com*

JANUARY

Monday 10

Tuesday 11

Wednesday 12

Thursday 13

Friday 14

Saturday 15

Sunday 16

Marshmallow clouds hover over the desolate beauty of
Badlands National Park, South Dakota
© iofoto/Shutterstock.com

JANUARY

17 Monday
○
Martin Luther King Jr. Day (USA)

18 Tuesday

19 Wednesday

20 Thursday

21 Friday

22 Saturday

23 Sunday

			JANUARY			
S	M	T	W	T	F	S
						1
2	3	4	5	6	7	8
9	10	11	12	13	14	15
16	17	18	19	20	21	22
23	24	25	26	27	28	29
30	31					

JANUARY

Monday 24

Tuesday 25
☾

Wednesday 26

Thursday 27

Friday 28

Saturday 29

FEBRUARY						
S	M	T	W	T	F	S
		1	2	3	4	5
6	7	8	9	10	11	12
13	14	15	16	17	18	19
20	21	22	23	24	25	26
27	28					

Sunday 30

JANUARY / FEBRUARY

31 Monday

Auckland and Nelson Anniversaries (NZL)

1 Tuesday
●

Chinese New Year—Year of the Tiger
World Interfaith Harmony Week Begins

2 Wednesday

Groundhog Day (USA, CAN)

3 Thursday

4 Friday

5 Saturday

6 Sunday

Waitangi Day (NZL)

FEBRUARY						
S	M	T	W	T	F	S
		1	2	3	4	5
6	7	8	9	10	11	12
13	14	15	16	17	18	19
20	21	22	23	24	25	26
27	28					

Sunset settles into Petrified Forest National Park, Arizona
© Sierralara/Shutterstock.com

FEBRUARY

Monday 7

Tuesday 8
☽

Wednesday 9

Thursday 10

Friday 11

Saturday 12

MARCH						
S	M	T	W	T	F	S
		1	2	3	4	5
6	7	8	9	10	11	12
13	14	15	16	17	18	19
20	21	22	23	24	25	26
27	28	29	30	31		

Sunday 13

Shadows creep over a cholla cactus garden in
Joshua Tree National Park, California
© Nick Fox/Shutterstock.com

FEBRUARY

14 Monday   *St. Valentine's Day*

---

15 Tuesday   *Lantern Festival (Last Day of Chinese New Year)*

---

16 Wednesday
○

---

17 Thursday

---

18 Friday

---

19 Saturday

---

20 Sunday

FEBRUARY						
S	M	T	W	T	F	S
		1	2	3	4	5
6	7	8	9	10	11	12
13	14	15	16	17	18	19
20	21	22	23	24	25	26
27	28					

FEBRUARY

Monday 21

Tuesday 22

Wednesday 23
☾

Thursday 24

Friday 25

Saturday 26

		MARCH				
S	M	T	W	T	F	S
		1	2	3	4	5
6	7	8	9	10	11	12
13	14	15	16	17	18	19
20	21	22	23	24	25	26
27	28	29	30	31		

Sunday 27

FEBRUARY / MARCH

28 Monday

1 Tuesday

St. David's Day
Mardi Gras

2 Wednesday
●

Ash Wednesday

3 Thursday

World Wildlife Day

4 Friday

5 Saturday

6 Sunday

First Sunday of Lent

MARCH

S	M	T	W	T	F	S
		1	2	3	4	5
6	7	8	9	10	11	12
13	14	15	16	17	18	19
20	21	22	23	24	25	26
27	28	29	30	31		

A wild pony grazes at Assateague Island National Seashore, Maryland
© Mary Swift/Shutterstock.com

MARCH

Monday 7

International Women's Day

Tuesday 8

Wednesday 9

Thursday 10
☽

Friday 11

Saturday 12

APRIL						
S	M	T	W	T	F	S
					1	2
3	4	5	6	7	8	9
10	11	12	13	14	15	16
17	18	19	20	21	22	23
24	25	26	27	28	29	30

Daylight Saving Time Begins (USA, CAN: 2:00 A.M.)

Sunday 13

Saguaros salute a jewel-tone sky in Saguaro National Park, Arizona
© Nate Hovee/Shutterstock.com

MARCH

14 Monday

Commonwealth Day • Canberra Day (ACT AUS) • Eight Hours Day (TAS AUS)
Labour Day (Victoria AUS) • Taranaki Anniversary (NZL)

15 Tuesday

16 Wednesday

Purim Begins at Sundown

17 Thursday

St. Patrick's Day

18 Friday
○

19 Saturday

20 Sunday

First Day of Spring

MARCH

S	M	T	W	T	F	S
		1	2	3	4	5
6	7	8	9	10	11	12
13	14	15	16	17	18	19
20	21	22	23	24	25	26
27	28	29	30	31		

MARCH

Monday 21

Tuesday 22

Wednesday 23

Thursday 24

Annunciation

Friday 25
☾

Saturday 26

		APRIL				
S	M	T	W	T	F	S
					1	2
3	4	5	6	7	8	9
10	11	12	13	14	15	16
17	18	19	20	21	22	23
24	25	26	27	28	29	30

Mothering Sunday

Sunday 27

MARCH / APRIL

28 Monday

29 Tuesday

30 Wednesday

31 Thursday

1 Friday
●

Ramadan Begins at Sundown
April Fools' Day

2 Saturday

3 Sunday

APRIL						
S	M	T	W	T	F	S
					1	2
3	4	5	6	7	8	9
10	11	12	13	14	15	16
17	18	19	20	21	22	23
24	25	26	27	28	29	30

A wooden walkway winds through a bald cypress grove,
Congaree National Park, South Carolina
© Natalia Bratslavsky/Shutterstock.com

APRIL

Monday 4

Tuesday 5

Wednesday 6

Thursday 7

Friday 8

Saturday 9 ☽

Palm Sunday

Sunday 10

MAY

S	M	T	W	T	F	S
1	2	3	4	5	6	7
8	9	10	11	12	13	14
15	16	17	18	19	20	21
22	23	24	25	26	27	28
29	30	31				

Sunrise and a horizon within reach,
Cape Cod National Seashore, Massachusetts
© Danita Delimont/Shutterstock.com

APRIL

11 Monday

12 Tuesday

13 Wednesday

14 Thursday

15 Friday

Passover Begins at Sundown
Good Friday

16 Saturday ○

Easter Saturday

17 Sunday

Easter Sunday

		APRIL				
S	M	T	W	T	F	S
					1	2
3	4	5	6	7	8	9
10	11	12	13	14	15	16
17	18	19	20	21	22	23
24	25	26	27	28	29	30

APRIL

Tax Day (USA)
Easter Monday

Monday 18

Easter Tuesday (TAS AUS)
Southland Anniversary (NZL)

Tuesday 19

Wednesday 20

Queen Elizabeth II's Birthday

Thursday 21

Orthodox Good Friday
Earth Day

Friday 22

Last Day of Passover
St. George's Day

Saturday 23
☾

			MAY			
S	M	T	W	T	F	S
1	2	3	4	5	6	7
8	9	10	11	12	13	14
15	16	17	18	19	20	21
22	23	24	25	26	27	28
29	30	31				

Orthodox Easter

Sunday 24

APRIL / MAY

25 Monday   *Anzac Day (AUS, NZL)*

26 Tuesday

27 Wednesday   *Administrative Professionals Day*
                        Holocaust Remembrance Day Begins at Sundown

28 Thursday

29 Friday   *National Arbor Day (USA)*

30 Saturday

1 Sunday   *May Day*
                                           Fête du Travail (FRA)

MAY						
S	M	T	W	T	F	S
1	2	3	4	5	6	7
8	9	10	11	12	13	14
15	16	17	18	19	20	21
22	23	24	25	26	27	28
29	30	31				

A hilltop view of history from Little Round Top,
Gettysburg National Military Park, Pennsylvania
© Jon Bilous/Shutterstock.com

MAY

Monday 2

Tuesday 3

Wednesday 4

Thursday 5

Friday 6

Saturday 7

JUNE						
S	M	T	W	T	F	S
			1	2	3	4
5	6	7	8	9	10	11
12	13	14	15	16	17	18
19	20	21	22	23	24	25
26	27	28	29	30		

Mother's Day

Sunday 8

Mountain laurel blooms at the Thoroughfare Overlook
on Skyline Drive, Shenandoah National Park, Virginia
© Jon Bilous/Shutterstock.com

MAY

9 Monday
☽

10 Tuesday

11 Wednesday

12 Thursday   *International Nurses Day*

13 Friday

14 Saturday

15 Sunday

			MAY			
S	M	T	W	T	F	S
1	2	3	4	5	6	7
8	9	10	11	12	13	14
15	16	17	18	19	20	21
22	23	24	25	26	27	28
29	30	31				

MAY

Monday 16
○

Tuesday 17

Lag BaOmer Begins at Sundown

Wednesday 18

Thursday 19

Friday 20

Armed Forces Day (USA)

Saturday 21

Sunday 22
☾

			JUNE			
S	M	T	W	T	F	S
			1	2	3	4
5	6	7	8	9	10	11
12	13	14	15	16	17	18
19	20	21	22	23	24	25
26	27	28	29	30		

MAY

23 Monday   *Victoria Day (CAN)*

---

24 Tuesday

---

25 Wednesday

---

26 Thursday   *Ascension*

---

27 Friday

---

28 Saturday

---

29 Sunday   *Fête des Mères (FRA)*

			MAY			
S	M	T	W	T	F	S
1	2	3	4	5	6	7
8	9	10	11	12	13	14
15	16	17	18	19	20	21
22	23	24	25	26	27	28
29	30	31				

Yosemite Falls plunges earthward to Yosemite Valley,
Yosemite National Park, California
© Radomir Rezny/Shutterstock.com

MAY / JUNE

Monday ● **30**

Tuesday **31**

Wednesday **1**

Thursday **2**

Friday **3**

Saturday **4**

			JUNE			
S	M	T	W	T	F	S
			1	2	3	4
5	6	7	8	9	10	11
12	13	14	15	16	17	18
19	20	21	22	23	24	25
26	27	28	29	30		

Pentecost
World Environment Day

Sunday **5**

The road not taken through lush woods, Shenandoah National Park, Virginia
© Jon Bilous/Shutterstock.com

JUNE

6 Monday
Western Australia Day • Bank Holiday (IRL)
Queen's Birthday (Observed) (NZL)

7 Tuesday
☽

8 Wednesday
World Oceans Day

9 Thursday

10 Friday

11 Saturday
Queen's Birthday (Observed) (UK)

12 Sunday

			JUNE			
S	M	T	W	T	F	S
			1	2	3	4
5	6	7	8	9	10	11
12	13	14	15	16	17	18
19	20	21	22	23	24	25
26	27	28	29	30		

JUNE

Monday 13

Flag Day (USA)

Tuesday 14

Wednesday 15

Thursday 16

Friday 17

Saturday 18

		JULY				
S	M	T	W	T	F	S
					1	2
3	4	5	6	7	8	9
10	11	12	13	14	15	16
17	18	19	20	21	22	23
24	25	26	27	28	29	30
31						

Father's Day
Juneteenth (USA)

Sunday 19

JUNE

20 Monday

---

21 Tuesday
☾

First Day of Summer

---

22 Wednesday

---

23 Thursday

---

24 Friday

Fête Nationale / St. Jean-Baptiste Day (CAN)

---

25 Saturday

---

26 Sunday

			JUNE			
S	M	T	W	T	F	S
			1	2	3	4
5	6	7	8	9	10	11
12	13	14	15	16	17	18
19	20	21	22	23	24	25
26	27	28	29	30		

A welcome mat of lupines in Mount Rainier National Park, Washington
© C Rolan/Shutterstock.com

JUNE / JULY

Monday 27

Tuesday 28

Wednesday ● 29

Thursday 30

Canada Day

Friday 1

Saturday 2

Sunday 3

	JULY					
S	M	T	W	T	F	S
					1	2
3	4	5	6	7	8	9
10	11	12	13	14	15	16
17	18	19	20	21	22	23
24	25	26	27	28	29	30
31						

Sunset gilds the landscape surrounding Bass Harbor Head
Lighthouse, Acadia National Park, Maine
© Sara Winter/Shutterstock.com

JULY

4 Monday *Independence Day (USA)*

---

5 Tuesday

---

6 Wednesday

---

7 Thursday
☽

---

8 Friday *Eid al-Adha Begins at Sundown*

---

9 Saturday

---

10 Sunday

			JULY			
S	M	T	W	T	F	S
					1	2
3	4	5	6	7	8	9
10	11	12	13	14	15	16
17	18	19	20	21	22	23
24	25	26	27	28	29	30
31						

JULY

Monday 11

Tuesday 12

Battle of the Boyne / Orangemen's Day

Wednesday 13
○

Thursday 14

Bastille Day (FRA)

Friday 15

Saturday 16

Sunday 17

AUGUST						
S	M	T	W	T	F	S
	1	2	3	4	5	6
7	8	9	10	11	12	13
14	15	16	17	18	19	20
21	22	23	24	25	26	27
28	29	30	31			

JULY

18 Monday

19 Tuesday

20 Wednesday ☾

21 Thursday

22 Friday

23 Saturday

24 Sunday

JULY						
S	M	T	W	T	F	S
					1	2
3	4	5	6	7	8	9
10	11	12	13	14	15	16
17	18	19	20	21	22	23
24	25	26	27	28	29	30
31						

American history on a grand scale, chiseled into the granite of the Black Hills
National Forest, Mount Rushmore National Monument, South Dakota
© S-L Photography/Shutterstock.com

JULY

Monday 25

Tuesday 26

Wednesday 27

Thursday 28
●

Islamic New Year Begins at Sundown

Friday 29

Saturday 30

		AUGUST				
S	M	T	W	T	F	S
	1	2	3	4	5	6
7	8	9	10	11	12	13
14	15	16	17	18	19	20
21	22	23	24	25	26	27
28	29	30	31			

Sunday 31

Crimson-colored hoodoos, with Thor's Hammer at the center,
Bryce Canyon National Park, Utah
© *JeniFoto/Shutterstock.com*

AUGUST

1   Monday

Civic Holiday (CAN) • Bank Holiday (IRL, NSW, SCT)
Picnic Day (NT AUS)

2   Tuesday

3   Wednesday

4   Thursday

5   Friday
☽

6   Saturday

Tish'a B'Av Begins at Sundown

7   Sunday

Ashura Begins at Sundown

AUGUST

S	M	T	W	T	F	S
	1	2	3	4	5	6
7	8	9	10	11	12	13
14	15	16	17	18	19	20
21	22	23	24	25	26	27
28	29	30	31			

AUGUST

Monday 8

Tuesday 9

Wednesday 10

Thursday 11

International Youth Day

Friday 12
○

Saturday 13

Sunday 14

SEPTEMBER

S	M	T	W	T	F	S
				1	2	3
4	5	6	7	8	9	10
11	12	13	14	15	16	17
18	19	20	21	22	23	24
25	26	27	28	29	30	

AUGUST

15 Monday

Assumption
Yukon Discovery Day (CAN)

---

16 Tuesday

---

17 Wednesday

---

18 Thursday

---

19 Friday
☾

---

20 Saturday

---

21 Sunday

			AUGUST			
S	M	T	W	T	F	S
	1	2	3	4	5	6
7	8	9	10	11	12	13
14	15	16	17	18	19	20
21	22	23	24	25	26	27
28	29	30	31			

Morning makes way for the daily unveiling of
Devil's Tower National Monument, Wyoming
© Sulae/Shutterstock.com

AUGUST

Monday 22

Tuesday 23

Wednesday 24

Thursday 25

Friday 26

Saturday 27
●

SEPTEMBER

S	M	T	W	T	F	S
				1	2	3
4	5	6	7	8	9	10
11	12	13	14	15	16	17
18	19	20	21	22	23	24
25	26	27	28	29	30	

Sunday 28

Ancestral Puebloan cliff dwellings carved into the canyon
walls of Mesa Verde National Park, Colorado
© Sopotnicki/Shutterstock.com

AUGUST / SEPTEMBER

29 Monday *Bank Holiday (UK except SCT)*

30 Tuesday

31 Wednesday

1 Thursday

2 Friday

3 Saturday
☽

4 Sunday *Father's Day (AUS, NZL)*

SEPTEMBER

S	M	T	W	T	F	S
				1	2	3
4	5	6	7	8	9	10
11	12	13	14	15	16	17
18	19	20	21	22	23	24
25	26	27	28	29	30	

SEPTEMBER

Labor Day / Labour Day (USA, CAN)

Monday 5

Tuesday 6

Wednesday 7

Thursday 8

Friday 9

Saturday 10
○

OCTOBER						
S	M	T	W	T	F	S
						1
2	3	4	5	6	7	8
9	10	11	12	13	14	15
16	17	18	19	20	21	22
23	24	25	26	27	28	29
30	31					

Patriot Day (USA)
Grandparents Day (USA, CAN)

Sunday 11

SEPTEMBER

12 Monday

13 Tuesday

14 Wednesday

15 Thursday

16 Friday

17 Saturday
☾

Constitution Day and Citizenship Day (USA)

18 Sunday

SEPTEMBER						
S	M	T	W	T	F	S
					1	2	3
4	5	6	7	8	9	10
11	12	13	14	15	16	17
18	19	20	21	22	23	24
25	26	27	28	29	30	

El Capitan rises 3,000 feet (914 m) above the Merced River
and Yosemite Valley, Yosemite National Park, California
© f1 1photo/Shutterstock.com

SEPTEMBER

Monday 19

Tuesday 20

International Day of Peace

Wednesday 21

Thursday 22

First Day of Autumn

Friday 23

Saturday 24

OCTOBER						
S	M	T	W	T	F	S
						1
2	3	4	5	6	7	8
9	10	11	12	13	14	15
16	17	18	19	20	21	22
23	24	25	26	27	28	29
30	31					

Rosh Hashanah Begins at Sundown

Sunday 25
●

Bison, grizzly bears, moose, and elk all make their home in
Grand Teton National Park, Wyoming
© Lorcel/Shutterstock.com

SEPTEMBER / OCTOBER

26 Monday

27 Tuesday

28 Wednesday

29 Thursday

30 Friday

1 Saturday

2 Sunday

OCTOBER						
S	M	T	W	T	F	S
						1
2	3	4	5	6	7	8
9	10	11	12	13	14	15
16	17	18	19	20	21	22
23	24	25	26	27	28	29
30	31					

OCTOBER

Labour Day (ACT AUS, NSW, S AUS)
Queen's Birthday (Observed) (Qland)

Monday 3

☽

Yom Kippur Begins at Sundown

Tuesday 4

Wednesday 5

Thursday 6

Muhammad's Birthday Begins at Sundown

Friday 7

Saturday 8

Sukkot Begins at Sundown

Sunday 9

○

NOVEMBER						
S	M	T	W	T	F	S
		1	2	3	4	5
6	7	8	9	10	11	12
13	14	15	16	17	18	19
20	21	22	23	24	25	26
27	28	29	30			

OCTOBER

10 Monday

Columbus Day / Indigenous Peoples' Day (USA)
Thanksgiving Day (CAN)

11 Tuesday

12 Wednesday

13 Thursday

14 Friday

15 Saturday

16 Sunday

Shemini Atzeret Begins at Sundown

OCTOBER

S	M	T	W	T	F	S
						1
2	3	4	5	6	7	8
9	10	11	12	13	14	15
16	17	18	19	20	21	22
23	24	25	26	27	28	29
30	31					

A blazing sunset transforms the Mesquite Flat Sand Dunes into an
otherworldly landscape, Death Valley National Park, California
© Doug Meek/Shutterstock.com

OCTOBER

Simchat Torah Begins at Sundown

Monday 17
☾

Tuesday 18

Wednesday 19

Thursday 20

Hawke's Bay Anniversary (NZL)

Friday 21

Saturday 22

Sunday 23

NOVEMBER						
S	M	T	W	T	F	S
		1	2	3	4	5
6	7	8	9	10	11	12
13	14	15	16	17	18	19
20	21	22	23	24	25	26
27	28	29	30			

Fall foliage frames the far-off view of Longs Peak and Bear Lake in
Rocky Mountain National Park, Colorado
© Hale Kell/Shutterstock.com

OCTOBER

24 Monday

25 Tuesday
●

26 Wednesday

27 Thursday

28 Friday

29 Saturday

30 Sunday

OCTOBER						
S	M	T	W	T	F	S
						1
2	3	4	5	6	7	8
9	10	11	12	13	14	15
16	17	18	19	20	21	22
23	24	25	26	27	28	29
30	31					

OCTOBER / NOVEMBER

Halloween • Marlborough Anniversary (NZL)
Bank Holiday (IRL)

Monday 31

All Saints' Day
Melbourne Cup Day (Victoria AUS)

Tuesday 1

☽

All Souls' Day

Wednesday 2

Thursday 3

Friday 4

Guy Fawkes Day

Saturday 5

Daylight Saving Time Ends (USA, CAN: 2:00 A.M.)

Sunday 6

NOVEMBER

S	M	T	W	T	F	S
		1	2	3	4	5
6	7	8	9	10	11	12
13	14	15	16	17	18	19
20	21	22	23	24	25	26
27	28	29	30			

NOVEMBER

7 Monday

8 Tuesday ○ *Election Day (USA)*

9 Wednesday

10 Thursday

11 Friday *Veterans Day (USA) • Armistice Day / Remembrance Day*
Canterbury Anniversary (Observed) (NZL)

12 Saturday

13 Sunday *Remembrance Sunday (UK)*

			NOVEMBER			
S	M	T	W	T	F	S
			1	2	3	4	5
6	7	8	9	10	11	12
13	14	15	16	17	18	19
20	21	22	23	24	25	26
27	28	29	30			

A view fit for a king, Wotans Throne at sunset,
Grand Canyon National Park, Arizona
© Pat Tr/Shutterstock.com

NOVEMBER

Monday 14

Tuesday 15

Wednesday 16 ☾

Thursday 17

Friday 18

Saturday 19

Sunday 20

DECEMBER

S	M	T	W	T	F	S
				1	2	3
4	5	6	7	8	9	10
11	12	13	14	15	16	17
18	19	20	21	22	23	24
25	26	27	28	29	30	31

Snaking through sandstone cliffs, the Virgin River
carves and shapes Zion National Park, Utah
© Bill 45/Shutterstock.com

NOVEMBER

21 Monday

22 Tuesday

23 Wednesday
●

24 Thursday   *Thanksgiving Day (USA)*

25 Friday

26 Saturday

27 Sunday   *First Sunday of Advent*

NOVEMBER						
S	M	T	W	T	F	S
		1	2	3	4	5
6	7	8	9	10	11	12
13	14	15	16	17	18	19
20	21	22	23	24	25	26
27	28	29	30			

NOVEMBER / DECEMBER

Chatham Islands and Westland Anniversaries (Observed) (NZL)

Monday 28

Tuesday 29

St. Andrew's Day

Wednesday 30 ☽

World AIDS Day

Thursday 1

Friday 2

Saturday 3

Sunday 4

DECEMBER

S	M	T	W	T	F	S
				1	2	3
4	5	6	7	8	9	10
11	12	13	14	15	16	17
18	19	20	21	22	23	24
25	26	27	28	29	30	31

DECEMBER

5   Monday

6   Tuesday

7   Wednesday   *Pearl Harbor Remembrance Day (USA)*

8   Thursday   *Immaculate Conception*
    ○

9   Friday

10   Saturday   *Human Rights Day*

11   Sunday

DECEMBER

S	M	T	W	T	F	S
				1	2	3
4	5	6	7	8	9	10
11	12	13	14	15	16	17
18	19	20	21	22	23	24
25	26	27	28	29	30	31

Sunset gives the freestanding Delicate Arch "rockstar" status in
Arches National Park, Utah
© *lunamarina/Shutterstock.com*